NAMIB DESERT, 1918

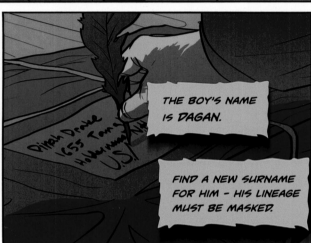

I AM ARMED, AND I AM READY.

IT'S JUST ME, SIR.

OH JAD, I'M SO GLAD YOU'VE MADE IT SAFELY.

IS EVERYTHING ALL RIGHT?

SNIFF

HE'S HERE!

BE SWIFT!

I'VE ALWAYS LOVED THIS PLACE.

NEVER CARED FOR THE...

INDIGENOUS FLAVORING THOUGH.

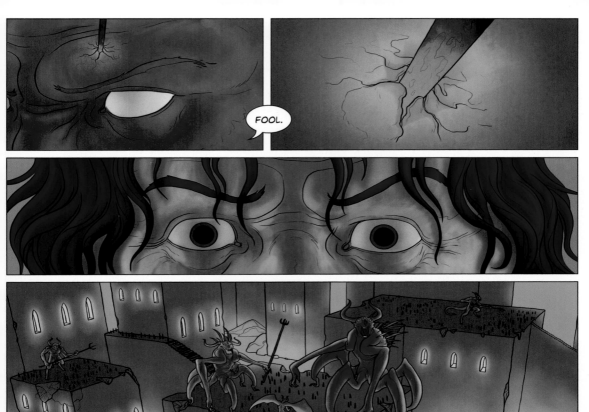

FOOL.

WHERE AM I...

WHAT MANNER OF EVIL...?

YOU TRULY *ARE* A DEMON.

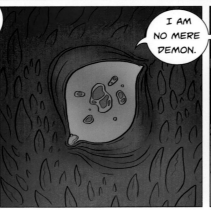

I AM NO MERE DEMON.

I AM A *DEITY.*

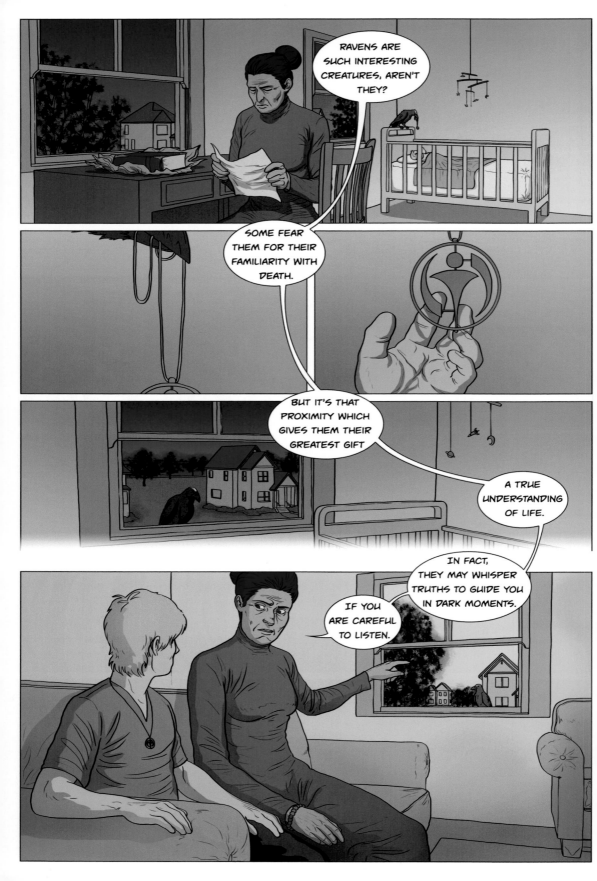

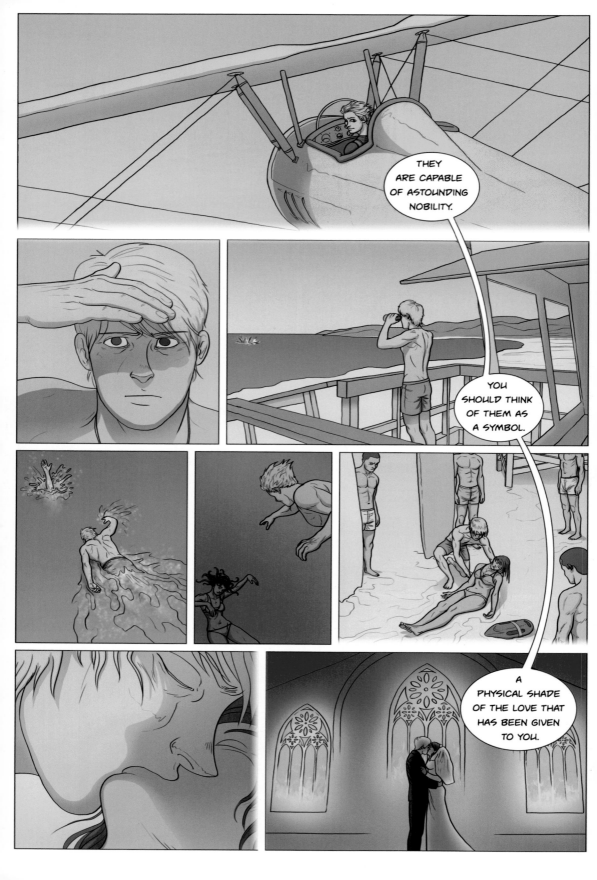

COMING UP ON KAZE.

YOU HIT THOSE ACK-ACK'S OR YOU'LL BE DISAPPOINTING THE SHIT OUT OF A LOT OF PEOPLE.

DISAPPOINTING IS ONE WAY OF PUTTING IT.

NO SHIT.

YOU TWO JUST MAKE SURE YOU KEEP IT STEADY FOR ME THIS TIME.

JUST 'CAUSE YOU CAN FLY DOESN'T MEAN YOU'RE A PILOT.

COCKY SMARTASS.

HEY, I EARNED COCKY.

WE ALL DID, HARRIS!

THERE'S A REASON WE BEEN UP HERE 17 TIMES.

AW HELL, I'M MESSIN' AROUND!

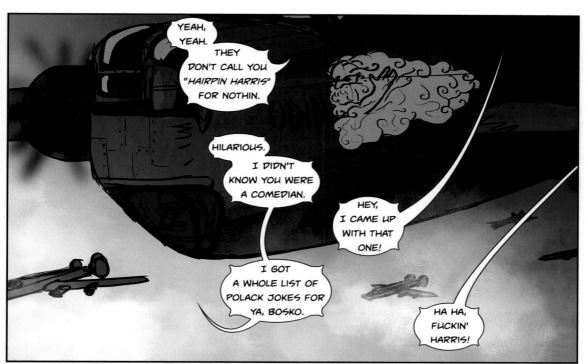

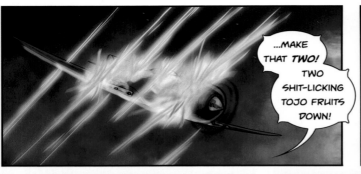

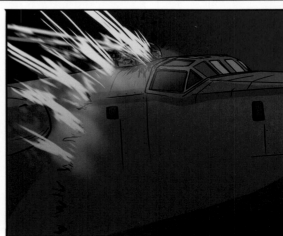

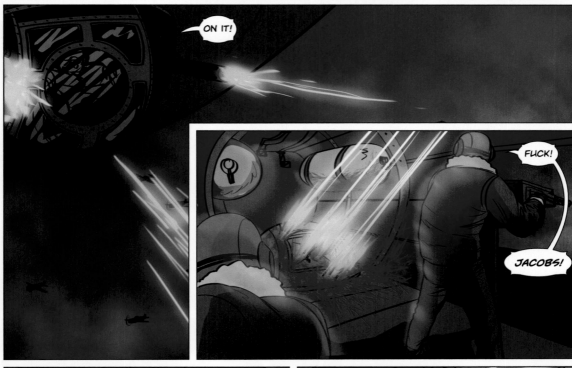

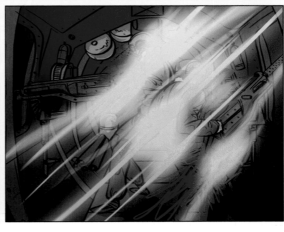

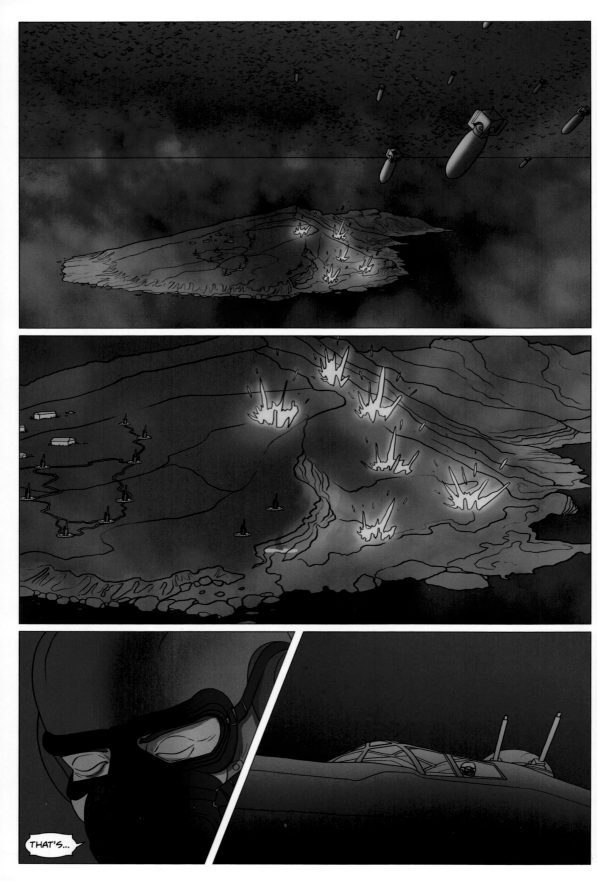

THAT'S...

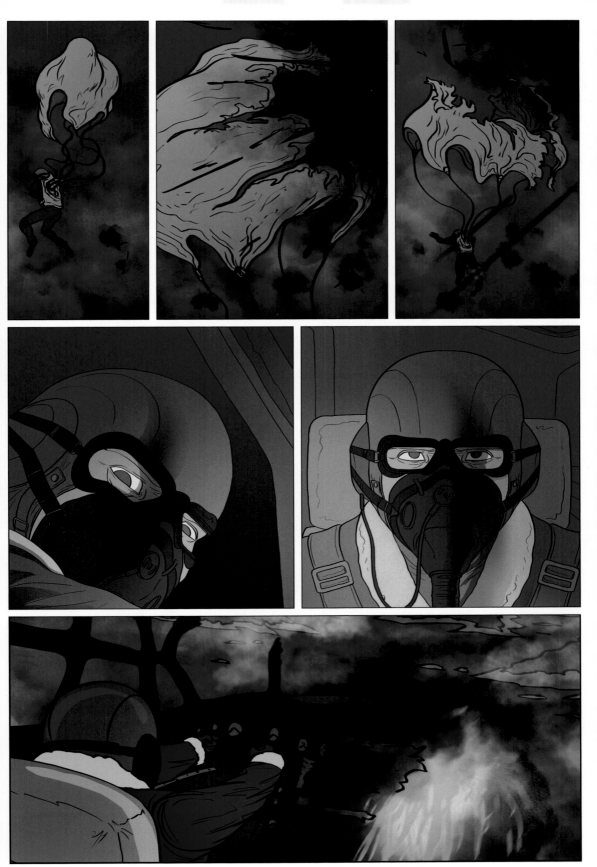

CHAPTER TWO

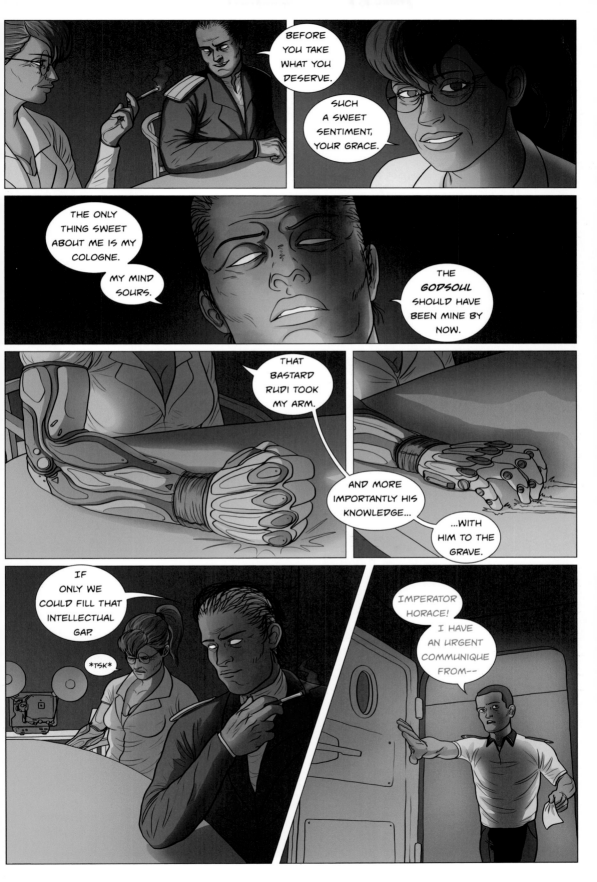

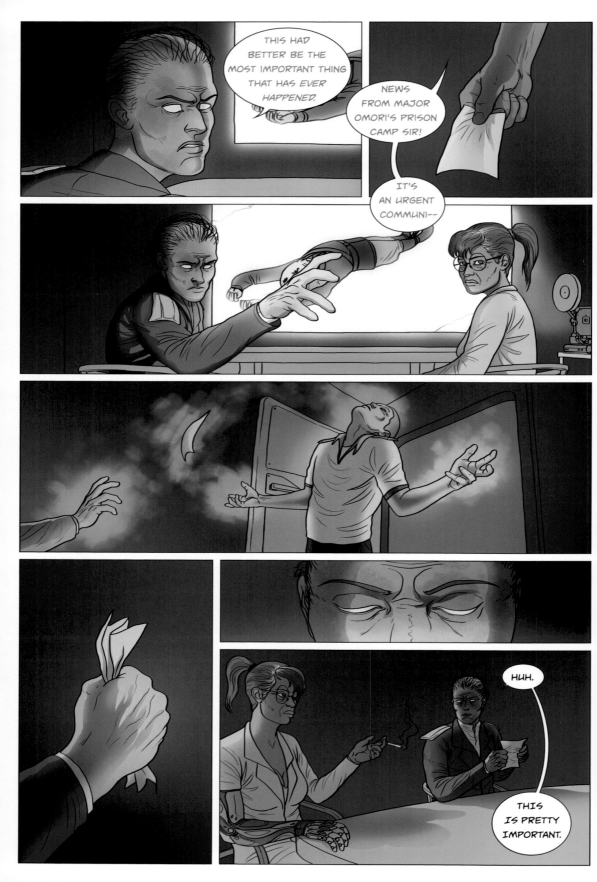

WE'RE ALL SET FOR LAUNCH.

GOOD.

IT SEEMS OUR SYCOPHANTIC LITTLE FRIEND FOUND SOMETHING VERY INTERESTING.

A GIFTED HETEROCHROMAT.

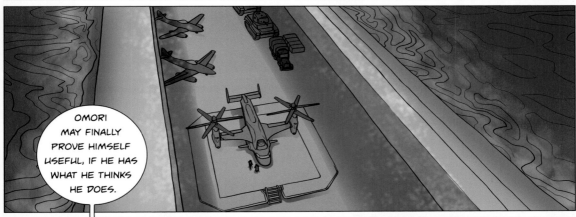

OMORI MAY FINALLY PROVE HIMSELF USEFUL, IF HE HAS WHAT HE THINKS HE DOES.

AND IF HE DOESN'T?

I HAVE NO TIME FOR USELESS THINGS.

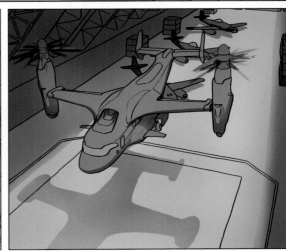

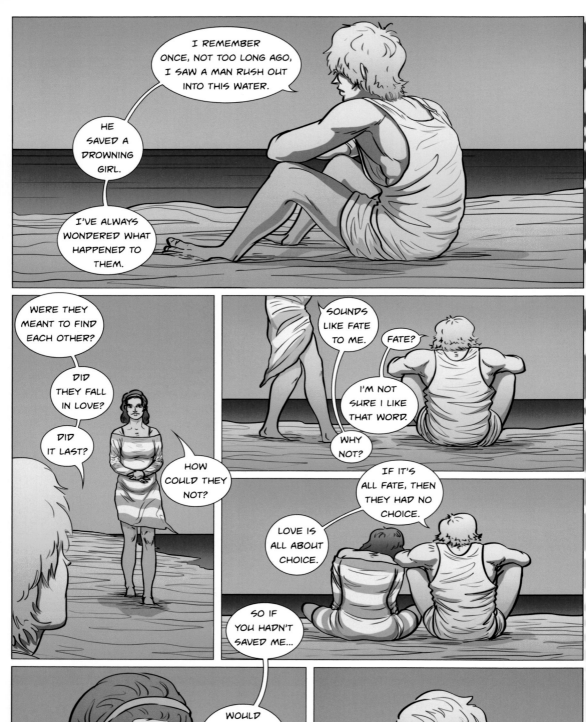

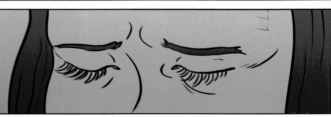

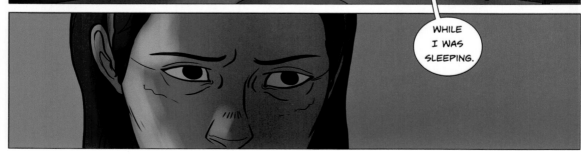

KEEP MOVING!

FALL BEHIND, YOU'RE DEAD!

YOU WERE TRANSFERRED HERE BECAUSE YOU ARE SPECIAL.

EACH OF YOU POSSESS SOMETHING WE BELIEVE MAY BE VALUABLE.

BUT YOU ARE ALSO LUCKY, DID YOU KNOW?

NOW, IT IS MY JOB TO DETERMINE HOW FAR YOUR LUCK WILL RUN.

I AM MAJOR OMORI.

THAT WILL BE THE NAME SIGNED ON YOUR DEATH CERTIFICATE.

OR...

YOUR TICKET HOME.

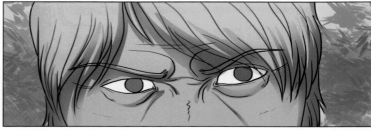

DO NOT FEAR.

I AM A REASONABLE MAN WITH REASONABLE EXPECTATIONS.

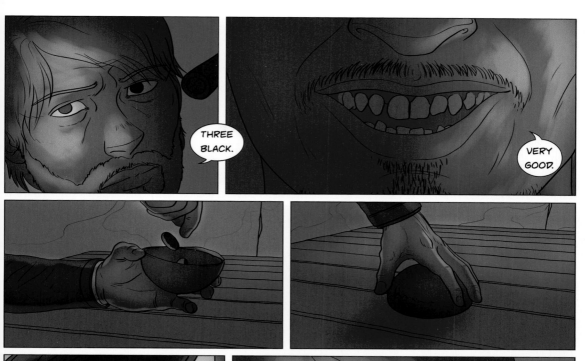

NOW, ANY LAST WORDS REGARDING YOUR FAMILY?

GO FUCK YOURSELF.

AND IF YOU ARE TRULY *NOT* THE ONE I AM LOOKING FOR, THE NEXT THING YOU WILL KNOW IS DEATH.

YOU MUST HOLD IT SAFE FOR HIM.

I'M TRUSTING YOU TO DELIVER IT TO HIS HANDS.

YOU SAY THAT DAGAN IS STILL ALIVE... HOW CAN YOU BE SO SURE?

HOW CAN YOU HAVE SO LITTLE FAITH?

IT'S NOT A MATTER OF FAITH.

IT'S A MATTER OF HOPE.

HOPE THAT HE'S OUT THERE.

HOPE THAT HE'S FIGHTING.

HOPE THAT HE WON'T QUIT.

I'M WORRIED THAT THE LAST OF MY HOPE IS GOING TO DIE WITH HIM.

THEN FEED THAT HOPE, CHILD.

THAT HOPE IS *YOUR* LIGHT TO KEEP ALIVE.

HIS LIGHT WILL BE DRAWN BACK TO YOURS.

THAT MIGHT BE THE ONLY THING...

AS FOR ME...

I'M FINISHED.

GET UP, YOU BASTARD.

WHAT DID YOU MEAN?

"THIS IS A TRIAL ONLY FOR ME."

WHAT DOES THAT *MEAN!?*

GET UP, GODDAMN IT!!

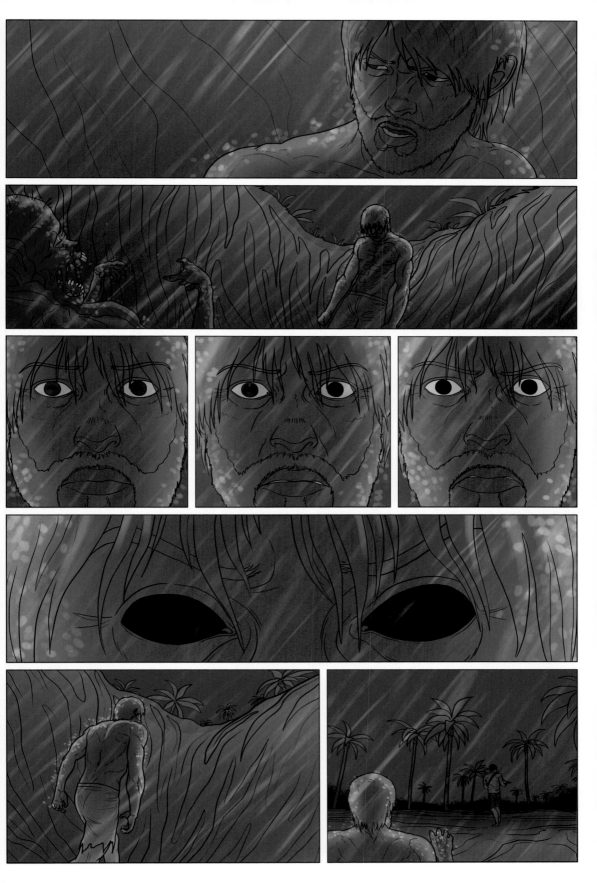

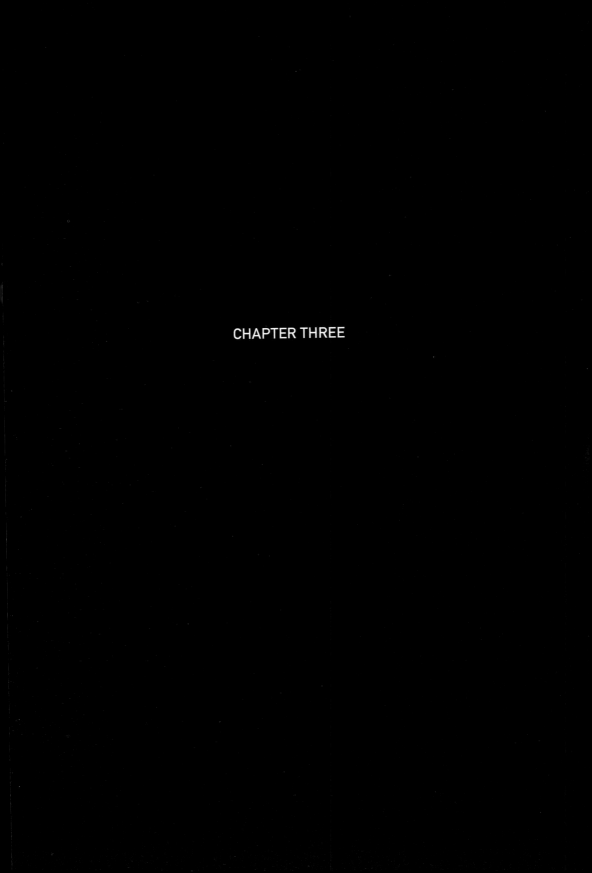

CHAPTER THREE

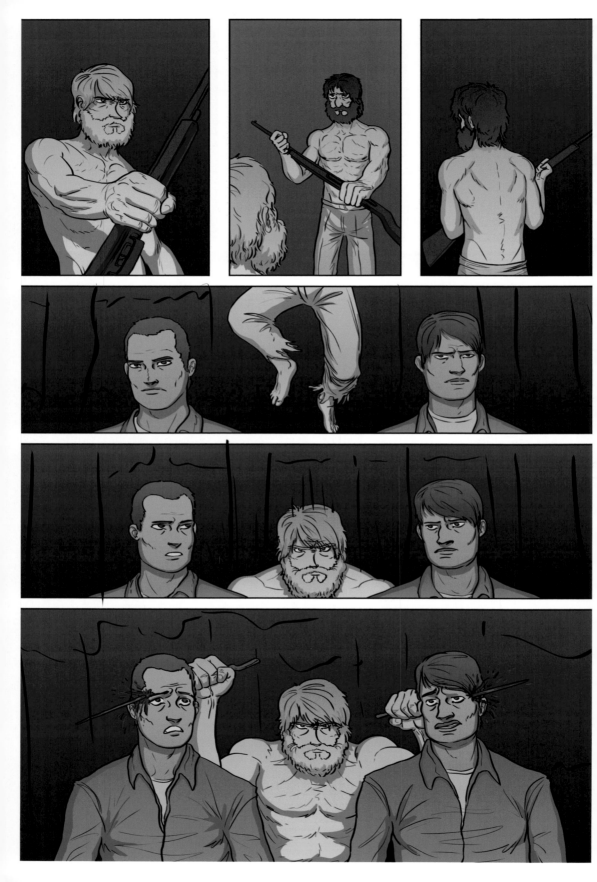

REMEMBER, IGNORE THE STENCH OF HIS DECAYING FLESH.

HE IS EASILY OFFENDED.

AND HAS A *VIOLENT* TEMPER.

IMPERATOR HORACE.

IT IS AN HONOR TO--

SPARE ME, OMORI. WAS THE TEST SUCCESSFUL?

UNFORTUNATELY IT WAS NOT, SIR.

TAKE ME TO THE BODY.

IT'S IN THE PIT.

I DON'T WANT TO WASTE YOUR TIME--

YOU'VE **ALREADY** WASTED MY TIME!

PLEASE, SIR, THE BODY PIT IS FILTHY.

WE HAVE PREPARED YOU SOME REFRESHMEN--

OH, OMORI...

HAVE YOU BEEN HIDING THINGS AGAIN?

OSIRIUM?

SIR PLEASE, IT JUST CAUGHT MY FANCY AND--

THIS BELONGED TO THE PRISONER DIDN'T IT?

I DON'T HAVE TIME TO KILL YOU, OMORI.

DON'T *MAKE* ME!

HOW PATHETIC.

RAAARGGHH!!!

THOSE EYES...

...AND YOUR SOUL RESISTS ME?

AH, YOU MUST BE THE ONE.

BUT HOW MUCH PAIN CAN YOUR *BODY* *TAKE!!?*

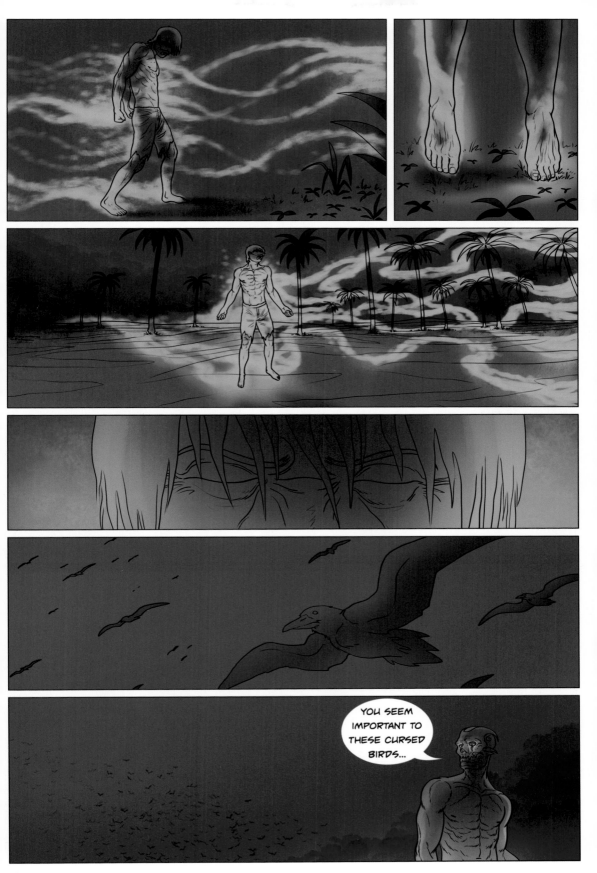

DESPERATE SOULS...

RENEW ME!

HM... THAT'S BETTER.

WHAT IS IT, RIPTON?

REPORTS ARE FLOODING IN...

THE BOMB'S TARGET IS NOW HIROSHIMA.

I SUSPECT THE AURELIANS ARE INVOLVED.

DAMN CULTISTS.

RETRIEVE THE HETEROCHROMAT!

I WANT HIS BLOOD, SO KEEP HIM ALIVE.

AND DISPOSE OF AS MANY OF THOSE *FUCKING* RAVENS AS YOU CAN.

I'LL HANDLE HIROSHIMA.

IMPOSSIBLE

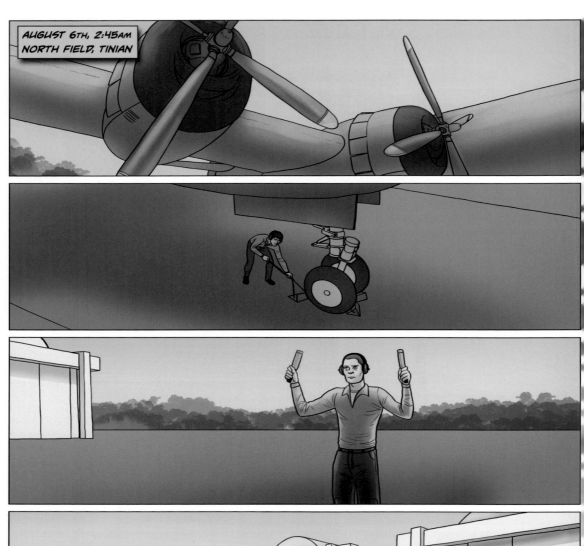
AUGUST 6TH, 2:45AM
NORTH FIELD, TINIAN

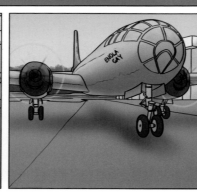

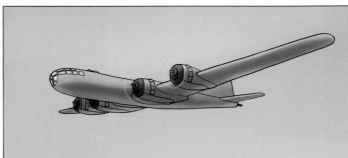

NOW HOW DO I GET TO THE DAMN THING.

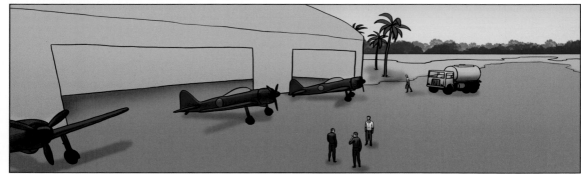

YUP. THAT'LL GET THEY'RE ATTENTION.

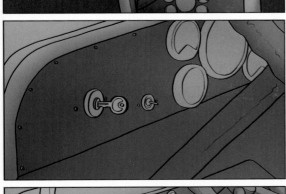

HUH.

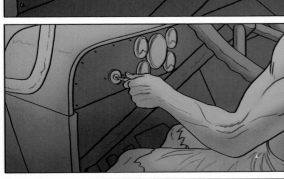
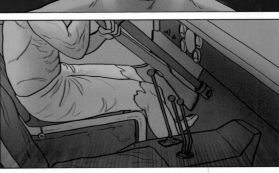

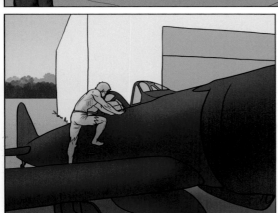

標高　燃料

のために

速度

OH RIGHT.

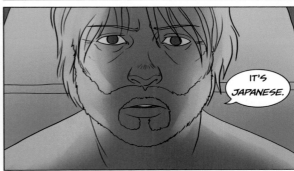

IT'S JAPANESE.

COME ON, HARRIS.

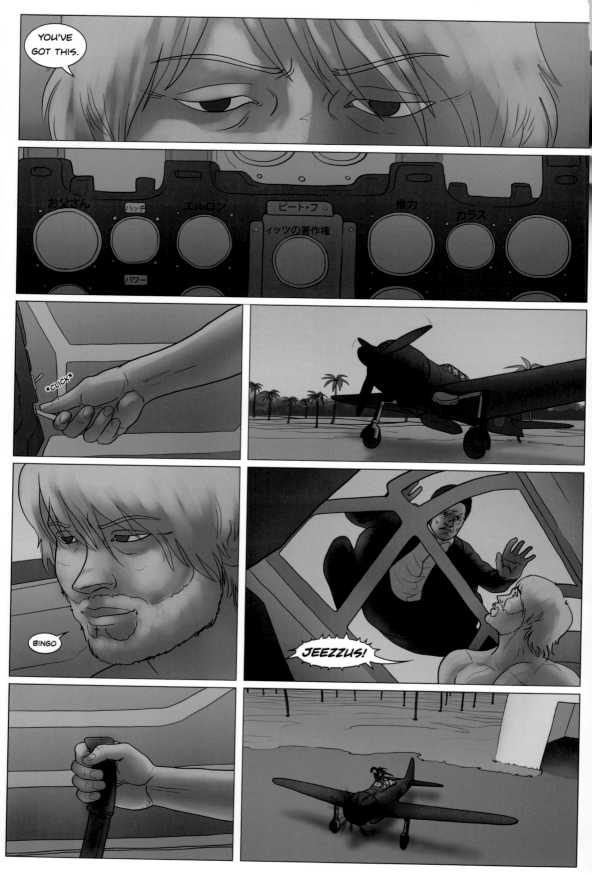

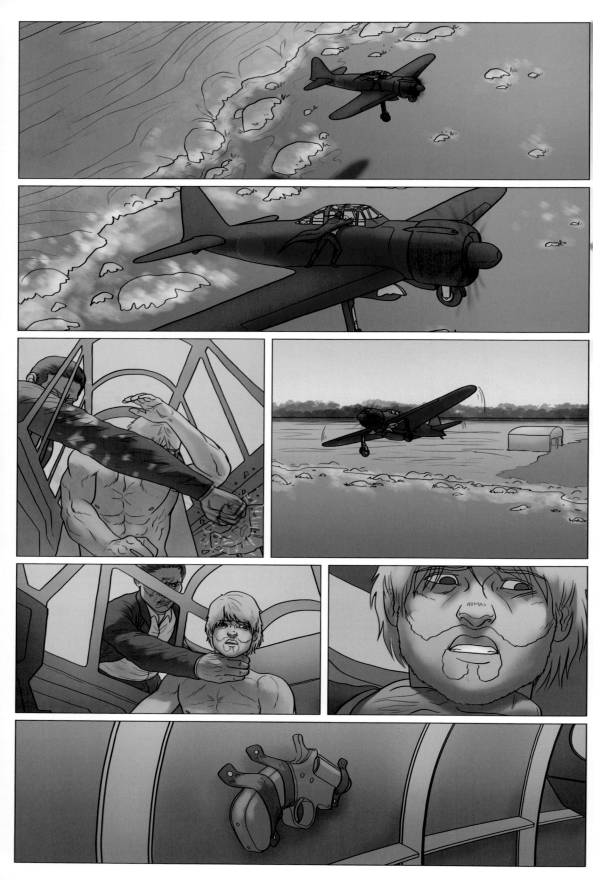

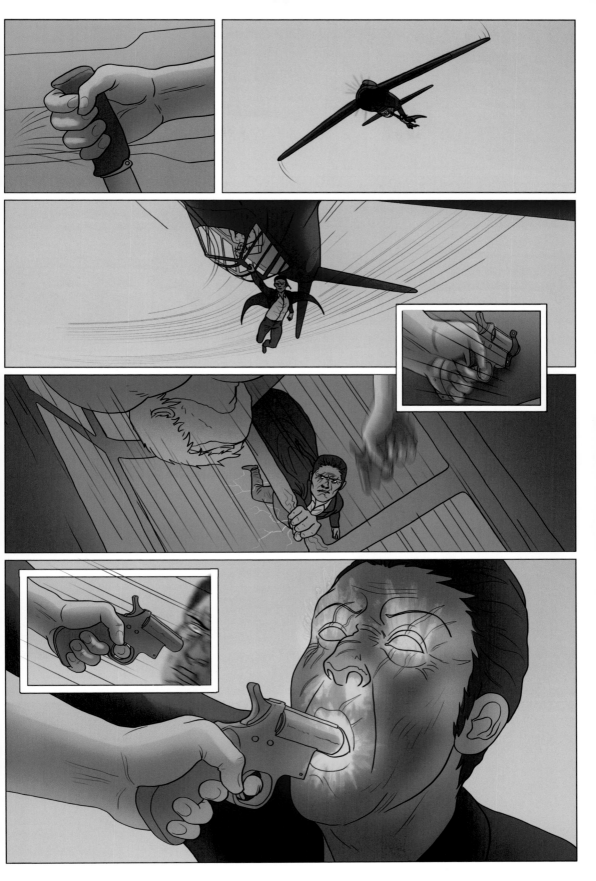

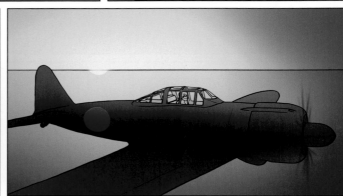
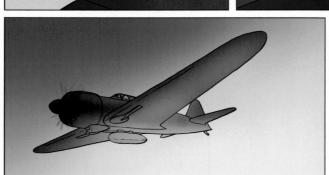

CHAPTER FOUR

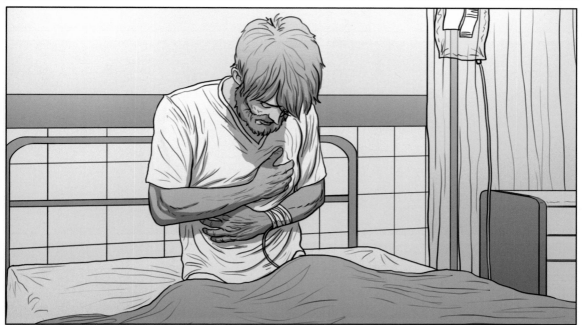

LOOKING FOR A PULSE?

DIDN'T THINK I'D MADE IT EITHER.

DON'T WORRY, YOU'RE ALIVE.

UNFORTUNATELY, YOU'RE ALSO IN AUSTRALIA.

That's no Jap kamikaze!

Eleanor...

...Eleanor...

It's Gareth, actually.

Gareth Callahan

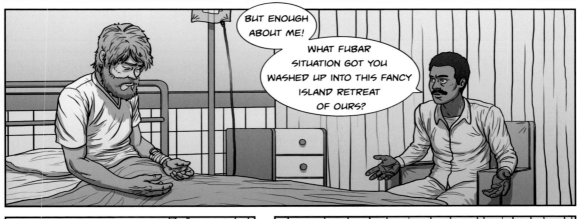

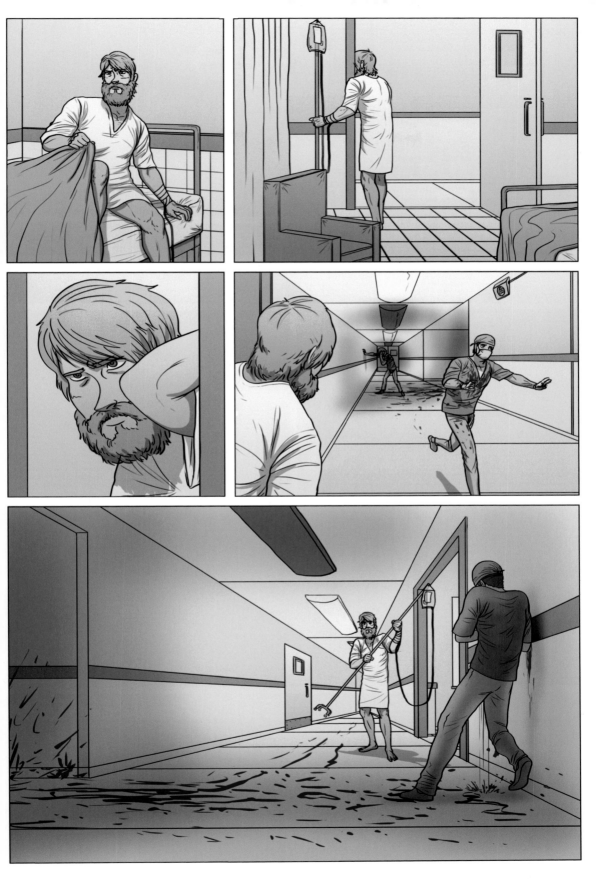

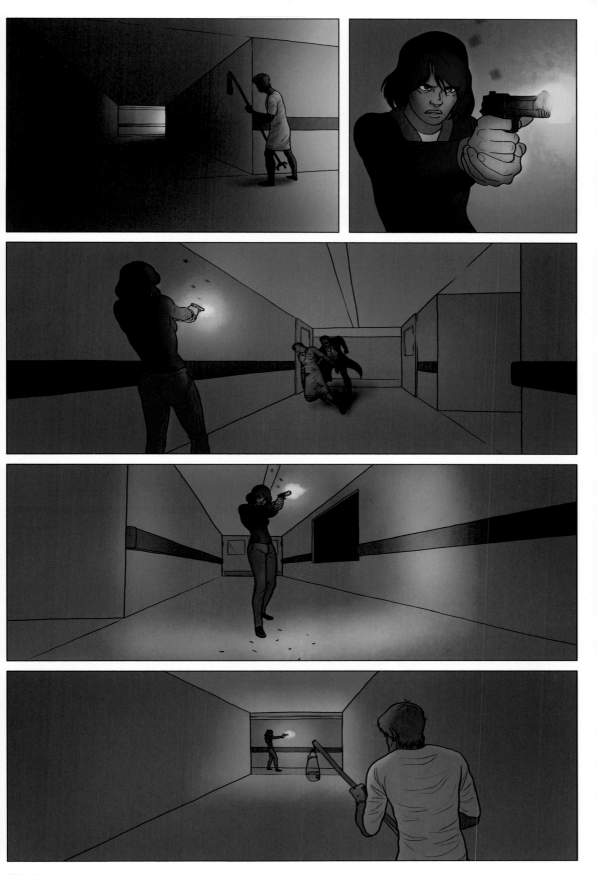

WE'RE NOT ON ANY OF THE FLIGHT RECORDS, FROM HERE ALL THE WAY HOME.

ANY FILES FROM OUR TIME AT THE HOSPITAL ARE WIPED OUT.

ONCE WE LEAVE THIS TARMAC IT'LL TAKE *HERBERT HOOVER* TO FIND OUR ASSES.

SO MY FAMILY IS SAFE?

SNUG AS A BUG.

I CAN'T THANK YOU ENOUGH, GARETH. I MEAN IT.

HEY, I'M SELFISH! A MYSTERIOUS MAN OF MANY TALENTS IS GOOD TO HAVE ON YOUR FAVOR LIST.

ANY TIME!

WHAT THE HELL?

THERE BETTER NOT BE A BLACK MAN IN THE MIDDLE OF THAT.

LOCKLEY... I BEEN WAITING FOR THIS A LONG TIME.

ME TOO, HONEY.

I BEEN PRACTICIN' BY BEATING UP ON A BRICK HOUSE.

I'LL GO EASY ON YA, *DAME!*

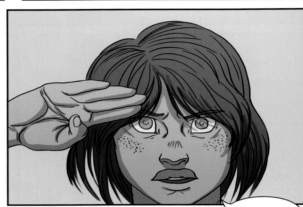

GRENIER AIR FORCE BASE, NH.

GAVIN, COME SAY HELLO TO YOUR FATHER!

HE WAS WORRIED YOU DIDN'T WANT TO COME HOME.

HEY CHAMP...

SORRY I'VE BEEN GONE SO LONG.

I KNEW YOU'D HOLD DOWN THE FORT THOUGH.

KEEP YOUR MOM SAFE.

EVEN THE CAR LOOKS WAXED.

YOU DID A HELLUVA JOB BEING MAN OF THE HOUSE.

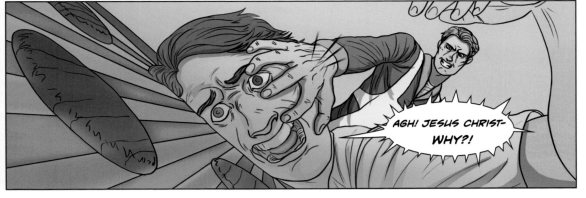

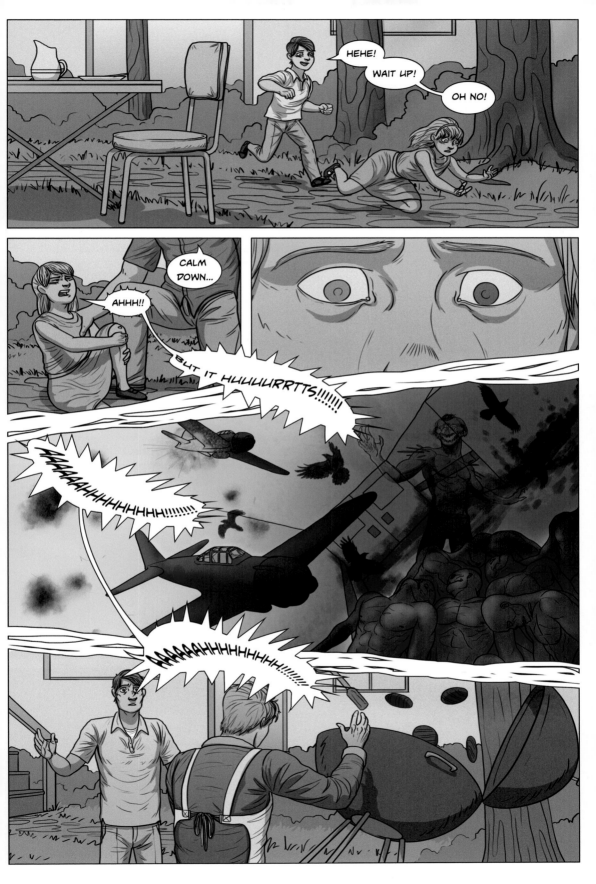

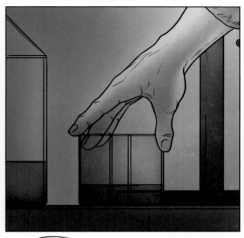

HONEY...

THE LEACHMAN'S JUST LEFT.

EVERYBODY SEEMED LIKE THEY HAD A GOOD TIME.

THAT WAS FUCKING EMBARRASSING.

MY SON SAW ME... SAW HIS OWN FATHER...

I CAN'T KNOW WHAT YOU'VE GONE THROUGH.

BUT WHAT I HAVE BEEN THROUGH HERE...

I ONLY MADE IT THROUGH BECAUSE OF HIM.

HE LOVES YOU.

I LOVE YOU.

AND NO MATTER WHAT HAPPENS, WE ALWAYS WILL.

GAVIN'S IN BED NOW, WHY DON'T YOU GO TUCK HIM IN?

HEY THERE BUDDY.

HAVEN'T DONE THIS IN AWHILE. HEH.

YAWN

YOU KNOW, THERE WASN'T A SINGLE NIGHT OVER THERE THAT I WASN'T THINKING ABOUT YOU AND YOUR MOM. WISHING I COULD BE SITTING BESIDE YOU LIKE I AM NOW.

I'M GLAD IT WORKED.

GLAD WHAT WORKED?

I THOUGHT ABOUT YOU EVERY NIGHT TO MAKE SURE YOU CAME HOME, AND IT WORKED.

SO IT WAS YOU, HUH?

YOU BROUGHT ME HOME, SON.

GOODNIGHT SON. I LOVE YOU.

LOVE YOU TOO, DAD.

THANKS DAD.

SURE, SON. FOR WHAT?

KEEPING US SAFE...

FROM THE BAD MAN.

THE BAD MAN? WHO'S THAT?

THE MAN OF...

GREEN FIRE.

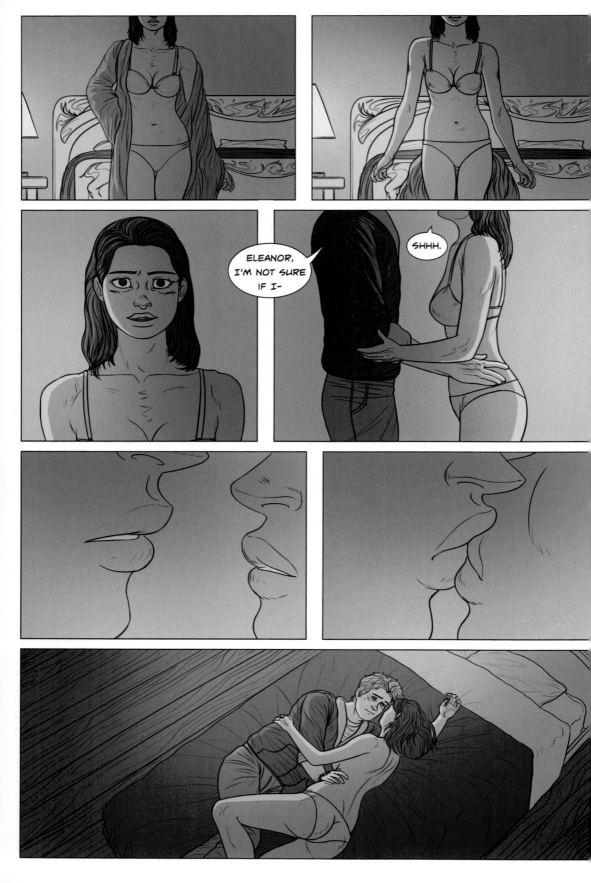

I'VE MISSED YOU.

SORRY YOU COULDN'T PLEASE HER...

MAYBE YOU JUST NEED A LITTLE...

SHOCK!

-OH, THAT MUST BE HIM NOW.

DAGAN, THERE ARE SOME MEN HERE TO SEE YOU.

A MR. COOPER AND MR EMERY.

...AND THEN YOU HIT THIS BUTTON TO RELEASE THE CLIP.

AH, MR. HARRIS. MR. EMERY AND I HAVE BEEN WAITING FOR YOU.

FUNNY, I DON'T REMEMBER INVITING THE FBI OVER.

WE DON'T GET INVITED OFTEN.

WE DO SHOW UP, THOUGH.

SO WHAT THE FUCK DO YOU WANT?

OKAY GAVIN, LET'S HEAD UP TO BED.

LET'S NOT GET OFF ON THE WRONG FOOT, NOW.

WE'RE JUST CURIOUS.

YOU WERE INVOLVED IN AN INCIDENT.

WERE YOU NOT?

DURING YOUR CONVALESCENCE AT THE GULIPILIL BASE HOSPITAL.

I ALREADY WENT THROUGH DEBRIEFING.

WE KNOW, WE JUST WANT SOME SPECIFICS.

FOR INSTANCE, SPECIFICALLY HOW DID YOU MANAGE TO ESCAPE THAT CARNAGE.

AND WHO HELPED YOU?

...HE'S GOT A KID WITH THE SAME PAIR OF EYES.

CREDITS

ART by

    JAMES ALLEN

WRITTEN by

    GRAHAM BOWLIN

    JESSE THREATT

ADDITIONAL WRITERS

    PETE HENDERSON

    DEREK HOCKENBROUGH

    MICHAEL SVOBODA

CREATED by

    PETE FITZ

Dark Matters is an independent endeavor. It was created by a team of hard working artists who devoted themselves to telling the best story possible. The hope, too, has always been that this project would grow into something that will stand the test of time, expanding into multiple mediums...say, a film series?

If you've enjoyed the journey thus far, know that we have written over fifteen hundred pages of story and are determined to get the next book out as soon as possible. If you have questions, comments, concerns, or if you'd like to help support our endeavor, please visit our website. If you're interested in working with or supporting our team get in touch via social media.

Pete Fitz

 @darkmatters00

 @darkmatterscomic

 darkmatterscomic@gmail.com

 Dagan Harris

 Dark Matters